At the Toy Store

By Lindsey Domke

Target Skill Consonant *Tt* /t/
High-Frequency Words *a, to*

Scott Foresman
is an imprint of

PEARSON

I am a little tiger.

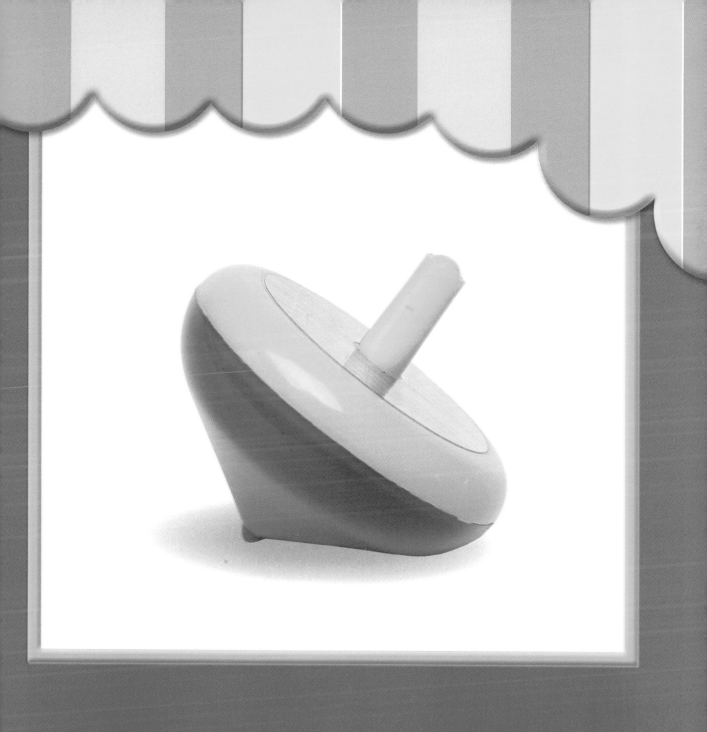

I am a little top.

I am a little turkey.

I am a little turtle.

I am Tyrannosaurus Rex.

I am a little teddy bear.

Toy Store

I am walking to the toy store.